SMART
SMARTER
SMARTEST

Brainy activities for fun learning

C000271733

Ages
7-8

First edition 2019

Offshoot Books

An imprint of Ratna Sagar P. Ltd.

GF–18, Virat Bhavan

Commercial Complex, Mukherjee Nagar

Delhi 110009

Phone: +91-11-47038000 / Fax: +91-11-47038099

Website: www.offshootbooks.com

Dear Reader,

Thank you for buying this book. We hope you enjoy every page of the book—and while you do that, please ensure that no one uses or transmits any part of this publication, in any form or by any means, without our prior written permission. You wouldn't want to offend the no-offence brand.

In case we haven't mentioned it before, we truly think that you are our favorite reader. Thanks for being a part of the Offshoot universe.

Have fun!

Love,
Team Offshoot

ISBN: 978-93-86362-86-5

Printed in India

Picture credits: www.shutterstock.com

ENGLISH

PHONICS

Every letter has a sound. The study of the sounds of letters and words is called PHONICS.

Hard and soft 'C'

The letter C has two sounds—hard and soft.
The hard C sounds like 'K' and the soft C sounds like 'S'.

cow

cent

cloud

camera

cupcake

cinema

circus

Hard and soft 'G'

The letter G also has two sounds—hard and soft. The hard G sounds like 'G' and the soft G sounds like 'J'.

giant

girl

garden

garage

geography

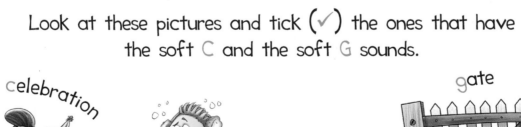

Look at these pictures and tick (✓) the ones that have the soft C and the soft G sounds.

celebration

cold

gem

gate

Why Y?

The letter Y has two sounds.
Sometimes it sounds like 'I' and sometimes it sounds like 'E'.

sky

curly

baby

bunny

spy

fly

merry

Knock! Knock!

Some words are naughty. They have silent letters.
Silent letters are letters that we don't say out loud.

light

write

knot

climb

lamb

Find the silent letters and circle them.

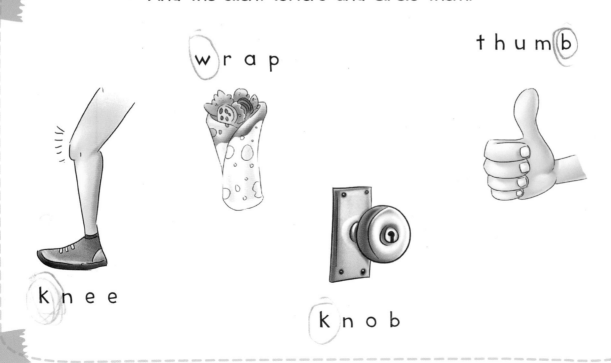

w r a p

t h u m b

k n e e

k n o b

VOWEL SOUNDS

Every vowel has two kinds of sounds—LONG and SHORT VOWEL SOUNDS.

In words with long vowel sounds, we can hear the names of the vowels—ay (A), ee (E), aye (I), oh (O), you (U).

In words with short vowel sounds, the vowels don't say their own name—bat, net, sit, cop, pup.

Examples:

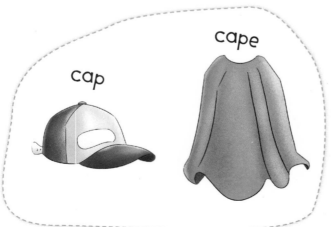

cap

cape

fat

face

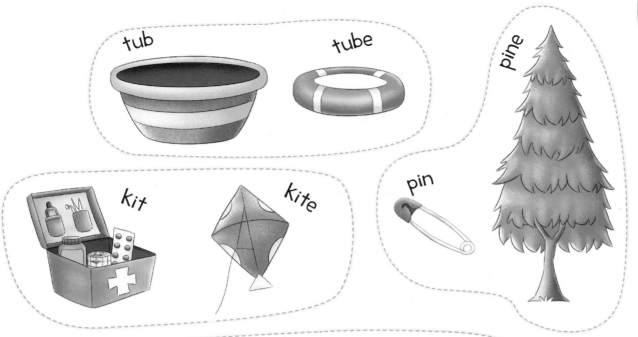

tub   tube   pine

kit   Kite   pin

bag

bake

Ask around and see how many long and short
vowel sound words you can find.

short vowel sound	long vowel sound
lamp	ligt
cushion	ape
bord	ate
picture	eight
glass	cute

Color the stars with the long vowel sounds.
Color the clouds with the short vowel sounds.

Vowel Sounds

cube

cup

cake

unicorn

can

ant

bus

cane

Circle the words with the long vowel sounds.

bat

key

umbrella

bee

ship

baby

jam

bed

home

egg

angel

dog

fish

bag

train

bake

Vowel Sounds

English

SYLLABLES

A word is made of many SYLLABLES. The number of times we break a word when saying it, is the number of syllables that word has.

2 syllables

pop-corn

ba-by

ra-bbit

pen-cil

pan-cake

tea-cher

2+3=?

pi-zza

sy-rup

Here are some 2-syllable words. Take a look at the pictures and write the missing names. Add the syllable break in every word.

mu-sic

tea-cher

ro-bot

se-ven

show-er

ap-ple

wa-ter

li-ttle

sham-poo

pl-ane

o-cean

coo-kie

3 syllables

Here are some 3-syllable words. Take a look at the pictures and write the missing names. Add the syllable break in every word.

u-ni-corn

um-bre-lla

choc-o-late

te-le-phone

pig-gy-bank

ham-bur-ger

la-dy-bug

pi-an-o

camrar

cam-ra-r

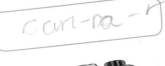

ma-gic-ian

di-no-saur

tri-ang-le

butt-er-fly

com-pu-ter

chocolate

po-lice-man

chocolate
overvon

bi-cy-cle

bas-ket-ball

Syllables

English

PREFIXES

A **PREFIX** is a word (or a letter) added to the beginning of a root word to make a new word. Some common prefixes are: un-, re-, in-, im-, dis-, pre-, tele-

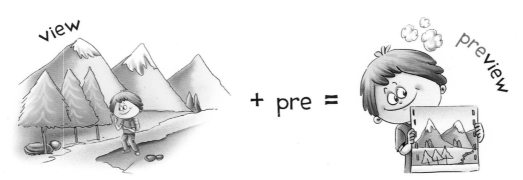

view + pre = preview

lock + un = unlock

like + dis = dislike

phone + tele = telephone

active

inactive

+ in =

write

rewrite

+ re =

Write the new words.

im	+	possible	=	impossible
in	+	justice	=	injustice
pre	+	fix	=	prefix
un	+	do	=	undo
dis	+	agree	=	disagree
tele	+	graph	=	~~tele~~ telegraph
re	+	do	=	redo

Coin new words

Make new words of your own. Add a prefix and
see what happens.

Old word	Add a prefix	New word
fix	pre	prefix
mum	my	mummy
tele	phone	telephone
Sug	fixes	suggix

SUFFIXES

A **SUFFIX** is a word (or a letter) added to the end of a root word to make a new word.

Some common suffixes are: -s, -es, -ing, -ed, -er, -est, -ful, -less, -ies, -ied, -ly, -y

pig   pigs

sleep   sleeping

run   running

dog   dogs

box

boxes

Suffixes

jump

jump**ed**

cloud

cloud**y**

big

bigg**est**

bunny

bunn**ies**

cold

cold**er**

tall**est**

fish

color

fish**y**

colar**ful**

tall

Coin new words

Make new words of your own. Add a suffix and
see what happens.

Old word	Add a suffix	New word
Jump	ing	jumping
nice	est	nicest
prety	er	pretier
mean	est	meanest
cute	er	cuter
short	er	shoter
hot	erter	hotter

Suffixes

STORY TIME

Write a story in your own words.

Your story must have:

Setting—Where ✓
Characters—Who ✓
Problem—What, Why, When
Happenings—What,
When—Beginning, Middle, End
Solution—How

One bright day in my back garden
all my friends were there with me in the
year "2023" T

Story Time

Story Time

COLLECTIVE NOUNS

A **COLLECTIVE NOUN** is the name given to a group of people or things. There are two kinds of collective nouns—common and uncommon.

Common collective nouns

a bunch of grapes

a flock of birds

a bouquet of flowers

a litter of puppies

an army of ants

a galaxy of stars

a class of students

a gaggle of geese

Look at these pictures and name the animals.

a swarm of

a school of

a herd of

Uncommon collective nouns

a crash of rhinos

a flight of swallows

a yoke of oxen

a cloud of bats

a walk of snails

a batch of cookies

a gang of turkeys

a raft of otters

a clutch of eggs

a caravan of camels

a stand of flamingos

a troubling of goldfish

a business of ferrets

a barrel of monkeys

a boil of hawks

Look at these pictures and name the animals.

a tower of

a zeal of

a pandemonium of

a waddle of

a parliament of

ABSTRACT NOUNS

An **ABSTRACT NOUN** is the name of a quality or an idea. Abstract nouns cannot be seen or touched, they define ideas and feelings.

Examples:

helpfulness

compassion

anger

wisdom

friendship

Kindness

fear

peace

music

wealth

eXcitement

Ask around and list 8 abstract nouns.

_____   _____

_____   _____

_____   _____

_____   _____

IRREGULAR PLURALS

Most plural nouns are created by adding -s or -es to the singular noun. Nouns that cannot be made plural by adding -s or -es are called **IRREGULAR PLURAL** nouns.

Examples:

child

children

hair—hair
woman—women
person—people
shelf—shelves
ox—oxen

So irregular

Write the singular noun for the following irregular plural nouns.

mice

feet

leaves

deer

sheep

fish

teeth

elves

IRREGULAR VERBS

IRREGULAR VERBS are verbs in which the past tense is not formed by adding -ed at the end.

Examples:

hear–heard

say–said

ride–rode

make–made

go–went

So yesterday

Look at the pictures and fill in the past tense.

sit_

drive–

see–

fall–

run–

think–

ADJECTIVES

ADJECTIVES are words that describe (modify) nouns. They tell us more about nouns and pronouns.

Examples:

angry

adorable

lovely

friend

happy

slow

My best friend and I

Describe yourself using five adjectives.

I am _free_   I am _happy_

I am _crazy_   I am _kind_

I am _naughty_

Write five lines about your best friend. Remember to use as many adjectives as possible.

_____

_____

_____

_____

_____

Adjectives

ADVERBS

Adverbs

> **ADVERBS** are also describing words—they describe (modify) adjectives, verbs and other adverbs.

Examples:

angrily

adorably

lovingly

friendly

happily

slowly

Write five sentences using adverbs.

_____

_____

_____

_____

_____

_____

_____

_____

_____

PREPOSITIONS

PREPOSITIONS are words that tell us where something is or when something happened.

Examples:

The boy is in the tub.

The food is on the table.

The girl is standing before the class.

The man is next to the bookshelf.

to   into   in   by   on

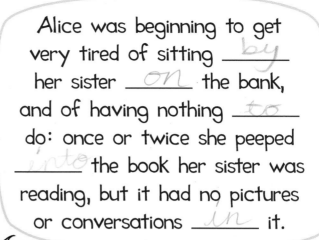

Alice was beginning to get very tired of sitting __by__ her sister __on__ the bank, and of having nothing __to__ do: once or twice she peeped __into__ the book her sister was reading, but it had no pictures or conversations __in__ it.

of   up   in

"And what is the use of a book," thought Alilce, "without pictures or conversations?" So she was considering __in__ her own mind (as well as she could, for the hot day made her feel very sleepy) whether the pleasure of making a daisy-chain would be worth the trouble __of__ getting __up__ and picking the daisies.

Prepositions

in   by   out   at   over   across   ~~to~~   out of   before   with   on   for   out of

Suddenly a White Rabbit with pink eyes ran close __~~to~~__ her. There was nothing so very remarkable _____ that; nor did Alice think it so very much _____ of the way to hear the Rabbit say to itself, "Oh dear! Oh dear! I shall be too late!" (when she thought it _____ afterwards, it occured to her that she ought to have wondered _____ this, but _____ the time it all seemed quite natural); but when the Rabbit actually took a watch _____ its waistcoat-pocket, and looked _____ it, and then hurried _____, Alice started _____ her feet, _____ it flashed _____ her mind that she had never _____ seen a rabbit _____ either a waistcoat-pocket, or a watch _____ take _____ it.

English

under down after out within across

Burning _____ curiosity, she ran _____ the field _____ it, and was just _____ time to see it pop _____ a large rabbit-hole _____ the hedge. In another moment _____ went Alice _____ it, never once considering how in the world she was to get _____ again.

to about down before to

The rabbit-hole went straight _____ like a tunnel for some way, and then dipped suddenly _____, so suddenly that Alice had not a moment _____ think _____ stopping herself _____ she found herself falling _____ what seemed to be a very deep well.

about   down   as   to

Either the well was very deep, or she fell very slowly, for she had plenty of time _____ she went _____ to look _____ her, and to wonder what was going _____ happen next.

SENTENCES

There are two kinds of sentences—simple sentences and compound sentences. A **SIMPLE SENTENCE** is a sentence that shows only one idea. A **COMPOUND SENTENCE** is a sentence that combines two ideas. A compound sentence is made up of two simple sentences joined together by a comma or a conjunction, such as, and, so, but, or because.

Examples:

SIMPLE SENTENCES

I like to draw.

The dog is barking.

COMPOUND SENTENCES

I like to draw and paint.

The dog is barking because someone is at the door.

Change the following simple sentences into compound sentences of your own.

Ava ran fast. She won the race.

Henry was hungry. He ate a whole burger.

It was raining. The children went out to play.

Simple and Compound Sentences

I finished my homework. I had time to play.

Jared was shivering. He was not well.

The magician performed a trick. A rabbit came out of his hat.

APOSTROPHE

The **APOSTROPHE** is used in two cases—in possessive nouns and in contractions.

Possessive nouns

In possessive nouns, the apostrophe is used when showing ownership.

Dylan's book (the book that belongs to Dylan)

Andy's bicycle (the bicycle that belongs to Andy)

Jamie's house (the house that belongs to Jamie)

Contractions

Some words in the English language are joined together with the use of an apostrophe.

I am = I'm
You are = You're
Did not = Didn't
She is = She's
I will = I'll

It is = It's
We are = We're
I have = I've
Cannot = Can't
Will not = Won't

Apostrophe

In a contraction, the apostrophe is put where a letter is dropped. In some cases, more than one letter is kicked out to make a contraction. Cannot becomes can't—one apostrophe is used even though two letters are dropped. Will not is another such exception—it changes to won't.

Make two sentences using the apostrophe to show ownership.

_____

_____

_____

_____

Fill in the blanks with the right contractions to complete this invite to your birthday party.

[I'm] having a party at my house on ([____]).

[____] my birthday. [____] be ([____]) years old.

[____] all invited. [____] be dressing up as our favorite characters. [____] going to be Merida. [____] made this invite all by myself. Mommy says [____] really proud of me.

[____] invited all my friends. Jordan [____] be able to come to the party. [____] be visiting her grandparents that week. Mommy says [____] kept my presents in the cupboard. I promised her I [____] take a peek. [____] wait for my birthday. [____] going to be really hard, but [____] keep my promise. [____] wait for my party. [____] going to have so much fun!

Apostrophe

Fill in the blanks with the correct possessive nouns.

Apostrophe

_____ roller skates are blue.

Ashley lost _____ book.

The _____ nest is on the tree.

The _____ hat is on the table.

The _____ ears are big.

That is _____ house.

A _____ house is called a kennel.

_____ hair is short.

A _____ shell is hard.

My _____ name is _____.

SYNONYMS

SYNONYMS are words that have the same meaning as each other.

burglar

thief

crook

stout

fat

chubby

rage

anger

fury

vehicle

car

automobile

devour

eat

gorge

repair

fix

mend

danger

hazard

risk

DANGER

kind

helpful

considerate

ill

unwell

sick

help

assist

aid

sorry

apologetic

remorseful

play

romp

frolic

Synonyms

ANTONYMS

ANTONYMS are words that mean the opposite of each other.

sunny — cloudy

calm — troubled

together — apart

right-side-up — upside-down

freeze — melt

Antonyms

Look at the pictures and write the missing antonyms.

float — sink

shallow — deep

coward — hero

friend — enemy

bitter — sweet

sad — happy

angel — demon

HOMOPHONES

HOMOPHONES are words that have different spellings, but sound the same. For example, pedal—peddle, hanger—hangar, etc.

Same sound, different spelling

flour
flower

ring
wring

berry
bury

manner
manor

Ask around and make a list of some homophones.

HOMOGRAPHS

HOMOGRAPHS are words that have the same spelling, but different sounds. For example, wind—wind, wound—wound, etc.

Same spelling, different sound

refuse   refuse

row

row

minute   minute

Homographs

Ask around and make a list of some homographs.

bear	down

HOMONYMS

HOMONYMS are words that have the same spelling and sound the same, too. For example, change—change, tire—tire, etc.

Same spelling, same sound

deck   deck

fall

fall

pen   pen

crane

crane

ruler

ruler

cool

cool

bat

bat

Ask around and make a list of some homonyms.

COMPOUND WORDS

Compound Words

COMPOUND WORDS are words made by joining two words.

Examples:

groundnut

highway

clockwise

lighthouse

dragonfly

firefighter

sunset

Compounded

Look at the pictures and write the compound words.

straw + berry = _____

foot + print = _____

friend + ship = _____

grass + hopper = _____

car + pet = _____

head + light = _____

house + boat = _____

gold + fish = _____

fire + place = _____

house + fly = _____

bird + house = _____

butter + fly = _____

candle + stick = _____

camp + fire = _____

Look at the picture and write the two words that make up its name.

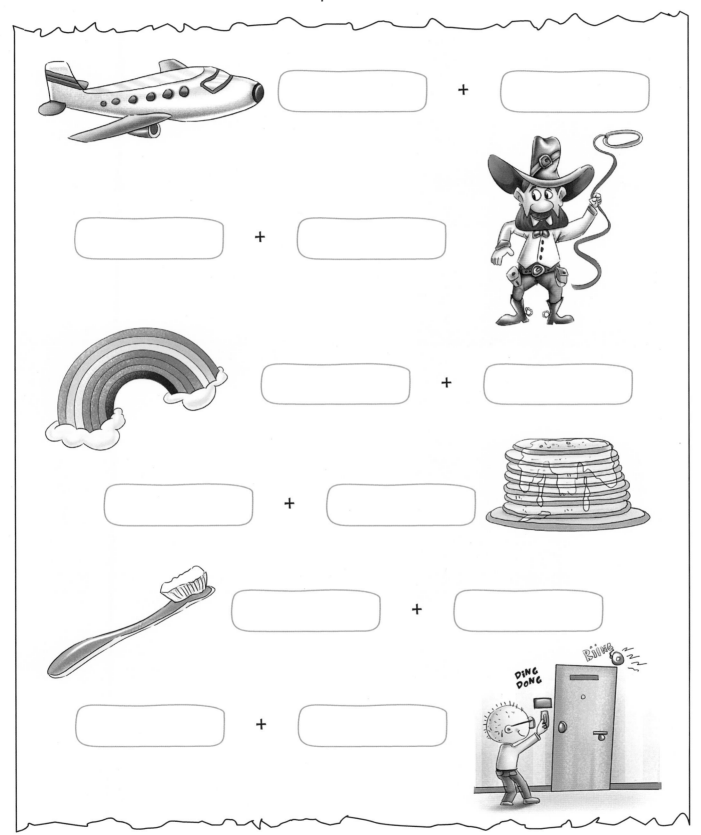

[   ] + [   ]

[   ] + [   ]

[   ] + [   ]

[   ] + [   ]

[   ] + [   ]

[   ] + [   ]

QUESTION WORDS

How to stretch a sentence

Who	The Sun
What	The Sun is shining
How	The Sun is shining brightly
Where	The Sun is shining brightly outside
When	The Sun is shining brightly outside today
Why	The Sun is shining brightly outside today because it's a sunny day

Now you try...

Who	The rain
What	The rain is dropping
How	The rain is dropping heavily
Where	The rain
When	
Why	

DAY AND NIGHT

As the Earth rotates, only one-half of it faces the light at any given time. The half facing the Sun has day and the half facing away from the Sun has night. This is how the rotation of the Earth causes DAY and NIGHT.

Night   Day

List any 2 things you see or do during the day.

1 play

2 trees

List any 2 things you see or do during the night.

1 sleep

2 stars

SHADOWS

A **SHADOW** is formed when a solid object blocks the path of light.

When our body blocks the light from the Sun, our shadow is formed. As the Earth moves, our shadow moves according to the position of the Sun.

our shadow in the morning

our shadow around mid morning

our shadow at noon

our shadow in the early evening

our shadow in the evening

Science

PHASES OF THE MOON

Look at the picture and color
the phases of the moon.

WEATHER

WEATHER is the daily state of our environment. It tells us how hot or cold, wet or dry a day is.

The main types of weather are...

Sunny

When the sun shines brightly in the sky, it is called a sunny day. Most days in summer are sunny.

Cloudy

When the clouds hide the sun, it is called a cloudy day. Cloudy days are usually cool.

Rainy

When the clouds in the sky have too much moisture, it rains. Rainy days are cool and wet.

Stormy

When thunder rolls across the skies and lightning flashes, it is called stormy weather..

Snowy

When the temperatures are very low, moisture from the clouds freezes and snowflakes fall from the skies.

Windy

When the winds blow with great force, it is called a windy day.

Match the things with the weather you use them in.

LIFE CYCLE

The stages a living thing goes through in its life are called its LIFE CYCLE.

Life cycle of a plant

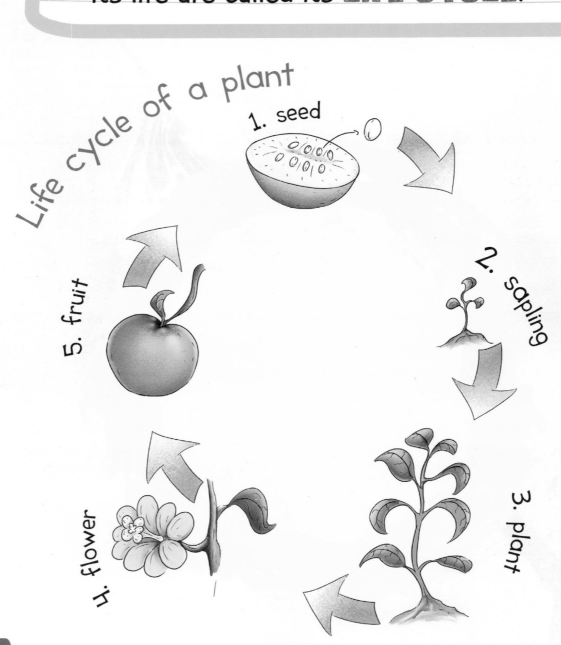

1. seed

2. sapling

3. plant

4. flower

5. fruit

Life cycle of a chicken

1. eggs

2. chick

3. chicken

Life cycle of a butterfly

2. caterpillar

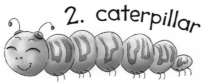

1. eggs

3. pupa

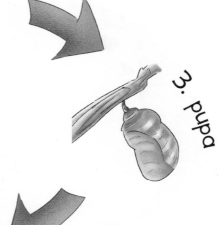

4. butterfly

Life cycle of a frog

1. eggs

2. tadpoles

3. tadpole with legs

4. tadpole with 2 legs

5. froglet

6. frog

Who's your daddy?

Look at the pictures and number the life cycle.

1

3

4

2

6

5

ADAPTATION

The natural home of a living thing is called its HABITAT. All living things change to adapt to their environment. ADAPTATION helps living things survive in their habitat.

Animals adapt in two ways—behavioral adaptation and structural adaptation. Behavioral adaptations are changes in an animal's behavior/habits that help it survive. Structural adaptations are physical changes in an animal that help it survive.

Some animals hibernate

bear

bat

 Some animals migrate

 monarch butterfly

 adelie penguin

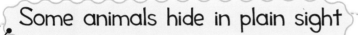 Some animals hide in plain sight

 chameleon

 stick insect

Some animals can store fat and energy for later use

 camel

Adaptation

Plants adapt in order to:

- get more sunlight—taller trunks and bigger leaves help plants absorb more sunlight

- protect themselves—thorns/spikes and a stinky smell help keep enemies away

- find more nutrients—some plants trap insects and absorb their nutrients

- attract insects—attractive colors and a nice smell helps plants attract more insects

- find more water—waxy stems, thin leaves, deep roots, above ground roots and spines help some plants find and store more water

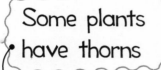

Some plants have thorns

Some plants have colorful flowers

Some plants can trap insects

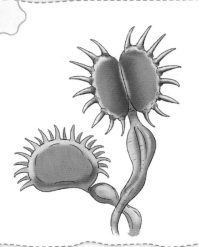

Some plants have long trunks and big leaves

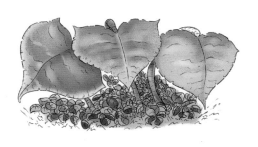

Some plants have above ground roots

SOLAR SYSTEM

Look at the Solar System and name the planets.

Mars

Earth

Mercury

venus

uranus

satern

jupiter

Solar System

Planet conundrum

Read the description and name the planet.

This planet is called the Red Planet.

Mars

This planet is called the Blue Planet.

earth

This is the biggest planet in our Solar System.

jupiter

This planet has rings around it.

~~Earth~~ saturn

This planet is also called the North Star.

polaris

This is the coldest planet.

Neptune

Name the planets

Look at the pictures and name the planets.

saturn

Mars

earth

jupiter

HEAT ENERGY

ENERGY is what makes things move and change. Energy is everywhere. There are five kinds of energy—mechanical, electrical, light, heat and sound.

Heat energy is created when an object is heated and its molecules begin to move faster due to the heat. Heat energy passes from hot objects to cold objects—that is why our hands get warm when we hold a mug of hot chocolate. The heat from the mug transfers to our cold hands and warms them up. We use heat energy to boil water, dry and iron clothes, and to stay warm.

Join the dots to discover the things that give us heat

Heat Energy

FORCE AND MOTION

FORCE is a push or pull on an object. Force causes **MOTION**—when we push or pull an object, it moves, changes direction or changes shape.

Modeling clay changes shape when force is applied to it.

A trampoline changes shape when force is applied to it and goes back to normal when no force is applied.

Pushing and Pulling

Look at the pictures and tick (✓) the ones that show 'push',
cross out (✗) the ones that show 'pull'.

Look at the pictures and tick (✓) the ones that show 'push', cross out (✗) the ones that show 'pull'.

Look at the pictures and tick (✓) the ones that show 'push', cross out (✗) the ones that show 'pull'.

Force and Motion

MATTER

MATTER is anything that occupies space and has mass. All matter is made up of tiny particles called molecules. There are three states of matter—solid, liquid, and gas.

The molecules in solids are packed close together. That is why solids keep their own shape.

The molecules in liquids are a little far apart from each other. That is why liquids take the shape of the container they are kept in.

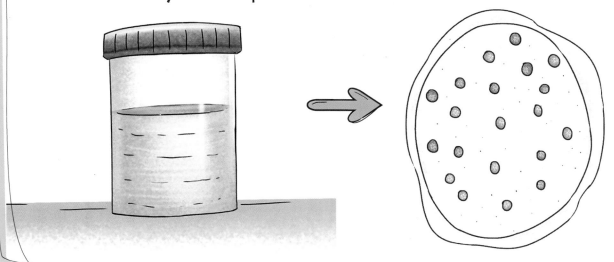

In gases, the molecules are very far from each other. That is why gases spread and fill the container they are kept in. Gases can change the shape and size of their container (example, a balloon)

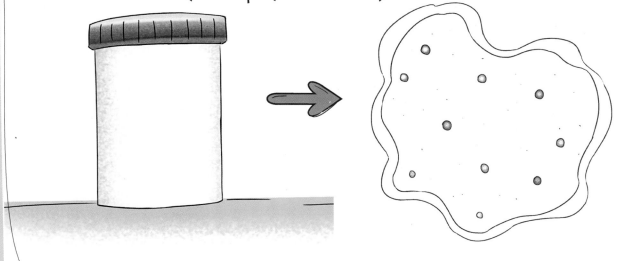

List 5 solids, liquids and gases around you.

Solids	Liquids	Gases
book	water	oxyge
~~penc~~ pencil	milk	carbon
ruler	juice	smoke
tub	blood	helium
table	mixture	nitrgen

Describe any two solids, liquids and gases from your list.
(Hint: size, color, smell, texture, shape, etc.)

Solids

_____

_____

_____

_____

Liquids

_____

_____

_____

_____

Gases

_____

_____

_____

_____

Matter

CHANGES IN STATES OF MATTER

Matter can change its form when heat is added to it. (Example: Ice—water—water vapor). Such changes are called CHANGES IN STATES OF MATTER. There are two kinds of changes— reversible and irreversible.

Reversible changes are those which can be changed back. Ice changing to water is a reversible change— because water can be changed back to ice on freezing.

  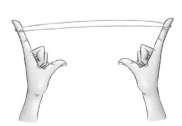

Irreversible changes are those which cannot be changed back. Cooking an egg is an irreversible change—once the egg has been cooked (boiled/poached/scrambled/fried) it cannot be changed back to its original state.

Write R for Reversible and I for Irreversible changes.

ROCKS AND SOIL

Soil is the loose upper layer of the earth's surface. All SOIL is made up of three kinds of particles.

Sand: Sandy soil has the largest particles, feels rough, comes in different colors and water can easily pass through it.

Silt: Silt has medium sized particles that are smaller than sand. Silt feels smooth and only a little water can pass through it. Silt is the most fertile kind of soil.

Clay: Clay has the smallest particles. It feels sticky and smooth, and does not allow water to pass through it. Clay is usually reddish-brown in color.

Sand, silt and clay together form the fourth kind of soil, which is called Loam. Loam is also known as agricultural soil and is used in farming.

Match the kind of soil with where it can be found.

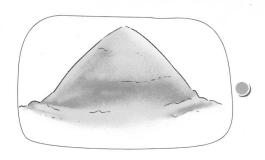

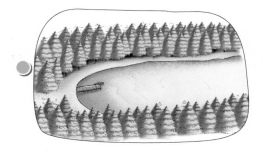

A **ROCK** is a solid made up of different kinds of minerals. There are three kinds of rocks.

Igneous

Igneous rocks are made when hot magma (lava from a volcano) cools quickly.

Sedimentary

Sedimentary rocks are formed when layers of sediment get squished together, like under the ocean.

Metamorphic

Igneous or sedimentary rocks that are changed by heat or pressure are called metamorphic rocks.

Let's rock

Find a rock and list its physical properties.

hard

soft

big

small

rough

smooth

color

shape

POLLUTION

When the environment is made dirty by chemicals and waste, it is called POLLUTION. There are different kinds of pollution—air, water, and noise.

Air pollution: When exhaust fumes from vehicles and factories mix with the air, it is called air pollution. Air pollution is very harmful to the health of everyone on the planet—people, animals and plants.

Water pollution: When chemical waste from factories and homes is drained into water bodies, the water gets polluted. Water pollution is also very harmful for all living creatures.

Noise pollution: Like air and water pollution, noise pollution is also a man-made thing. Vehicle horns, factory sirens, loud music, etc. are all examples of noise pollution. It is harmful to our ears. Noise pollution in the hills can even cause landslides and avalanches.

The Earth needs our help. There are some things we can do to prevent pollution and help save the environment. Color the clouds that will help save the planet.

waste water

save paper

plant trees

turn off the lights

watch less TV

turn off the tap

reuse things

donate clothes

buy less

carpool

FOSSILS

FOSSILS are the remains of plants and animals that lived a long time ago. Fossils tell us about the kinds of animals and plants that lived on Earth thousands of years ago. There are two main types of fossils—body fossils and trace fossils.

Body fossils are the remains of a plant or animal's body.

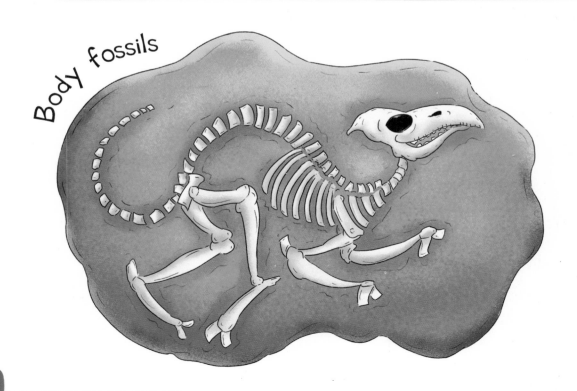

Body fossils

Trace fossils are the remains of things that tell us about the plants and animals that lived on Earth thousands of years ago.

Trace fossils

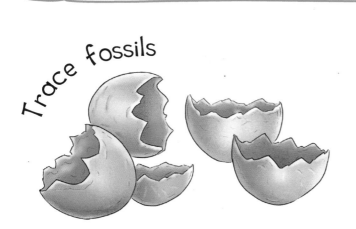

Make your own dinosaur fossil

You will need: some modeling clay, small dinosaur toys, a small glass

Fossils

Step 1
Take some modeling clay and roll it out.

Step 2
Use the glass to cut out a few small circles.

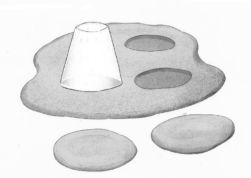

Step 3
Press your dinosaur toys on the circles.

Step 4
Remove the toys.

Voila! Your dinosaur fossils are ready!

Science

MATHS

ADDITION

ADDITION is also called putting together. The symbol for addition is (+)

Add the following:

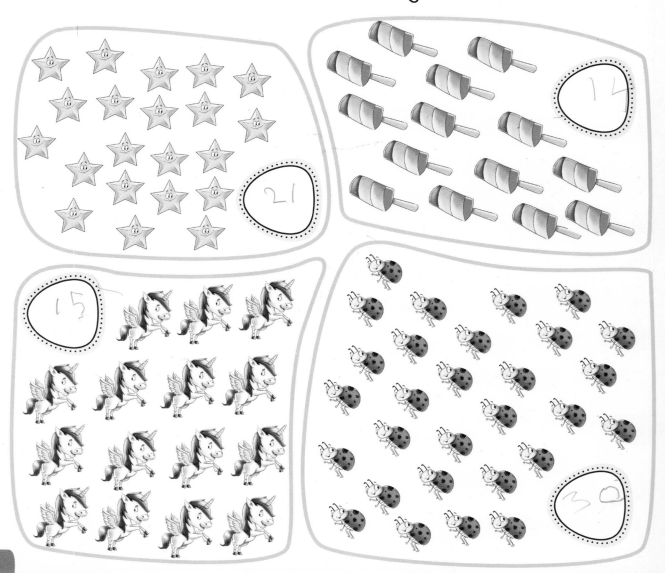

Addition

Color by numbers

Add the numbers and color the picture
according to the code.

8	⬤
12	⬤
19	⬤

SUBTRACTION

To subtract means to take away, or take from.
The symbol for SUBTRACTION is (−)

Subtract the following:

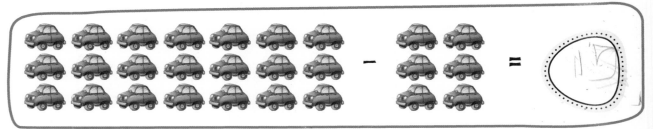

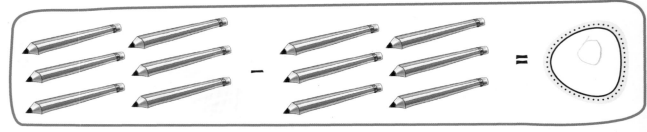

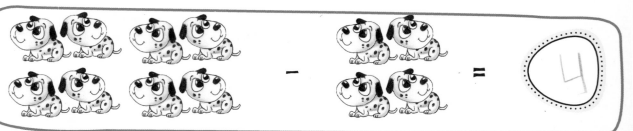

Subtraction

Color by numbers

Subtract the numbers and color the picture according to the code.

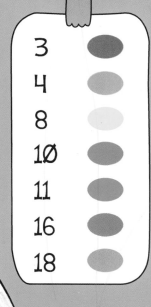

3	⬤
4	⬤
8	⬤
10	⬤
11	⬤
16	⬤
18	⬤

Subtraction

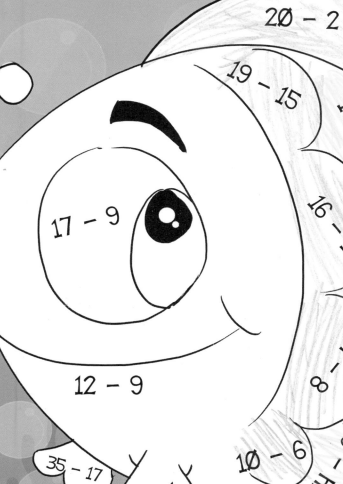

30 – 19

20 – 2

19 – 15

16 – 8

20 – 10

22 – 11

17 – 9

16 – 12

20 – 12

35 – 25

15 – 4

30 – 12

12 – 9

8 – 4

20 – 2

10 – 2

15 – 5

20 – 4

19 – 11

35 – 17

19 – 1

10 – 6

14 – 6

12 – 2

20 – 9

25 – 6

Math

MULTIPLICATION

MULTIPLICATION is also called repeated addition. When we add a number to itself a number of times, we multiply the number. The symbol for multiplication is (x)

Example:

3 groups of 2

3 × 2

= 6

3 groups of 3

3 × 3

= 9

Let's multiply

Look at the pictures, put them in groups and write the multiplication fact.

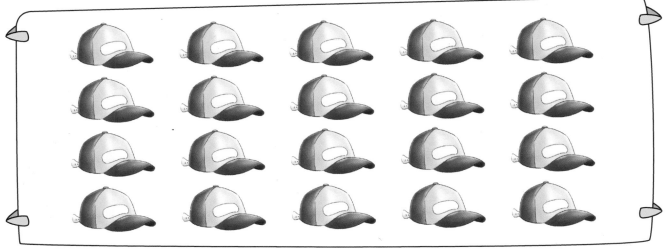

4 groups of 5

5 × 4

= 20

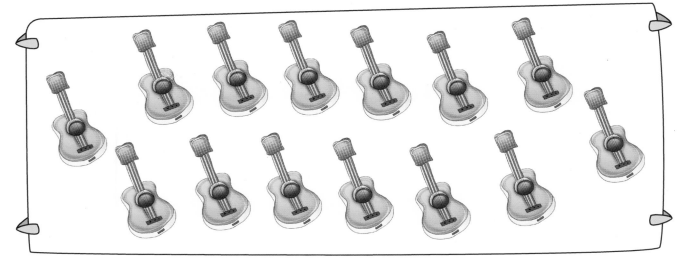

2 groups of 7

2 × 7

= 14

DIVISION

DIVISION means splitting something into equal parts or groups. Division is also called repeated subtraction. The symbol for division (÷)

For example, 12 can be divided into:

groups of 2

groups of 3

groups of 4

groups of 6

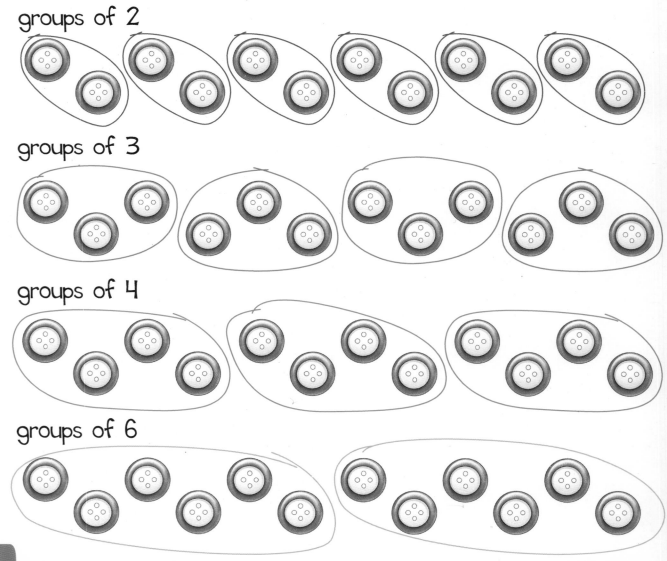

Divvy them up

Look at the pictures and divide them into equal groups.

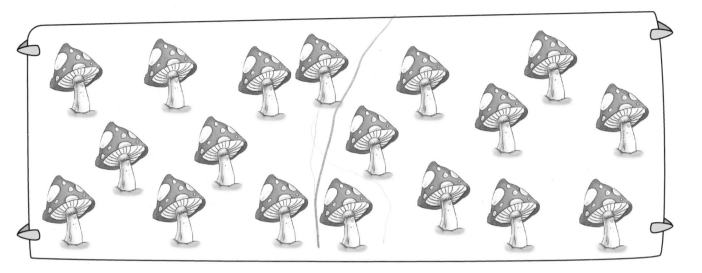

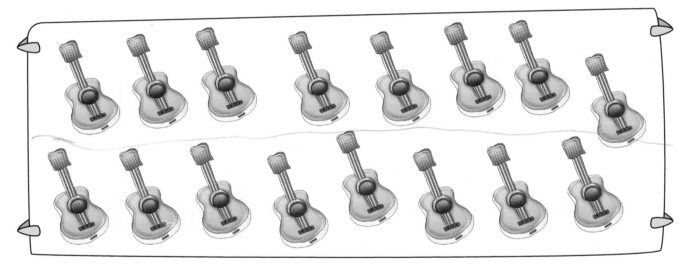

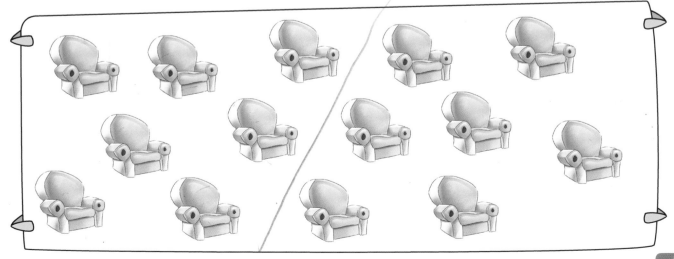

ROUNDING WHOLE NUMBERS

All natural, positive numbers, such, as 0, 1, 2, 3... are called WHOLE NUMBERS. Sometimes, we round whole numbers to the nearest ten or the nearest hundred to find an estimate.

Example:

Rounding up to the nearest ten.

Rounding up to the nearest hundred.

Well-rounded

Look at the numbers and round them up
to the nearest ten.

18   20   75   70

16   20   97   100

86   90   49   50

Look at the numbers and round them up
to the nearest hundred.

123   200   475   500

356   400   555   600

487   500   746   700

WORD PROBLEMS

1. Angel and Jackie have 5 dogs. How many legs do five dogs have?

2. There are 25 pig pens with 2 pigs each. How many pigs are there in all?

3. There are 10 plates on the table. There are 4 cookies on each plate. How many cookies are there in all?

4. Jose has 40 cookies. He shares them with three of his friends. How many cookies will each person get?

5. Aaron and Jamie order a pizza. It has 6 slices. How many slices will each get?

6. Dylan has 80 building blocks. He wants to divide them equally with his teddy bear. How many blocks will each get?

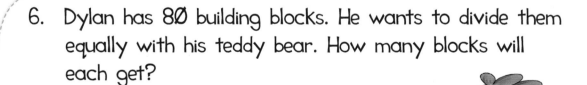

PLACE VALUE

The position, or place, of a digit in a number is called its PLACE VALUE. In the standard system, each place value is ten times that of the number to its right. That is why that place value system (base ten) goes ones, tens, hundreds, and so on.

Example:

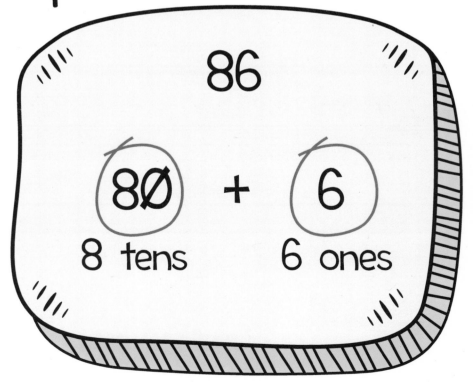

86

80 + 6

8 tens   6 ones

Know your place

Look at the numbers and write their place value.

 **97**   ⁹ tens + ⁷ ones

 **86**   ⁸ tens + ⁶ ones

 **81**   ⁸ tens + ¹ ones

1Ø   ¹ tens + ⁰ ones

 **17**   ¹ tens + ⁷ ones

28   ² tens + ² ones

 **79**   ⁷ tens + ⁹ ones

18   ¹ tens + ⁸ ones

 **35**   ³ tens + ⁵ ones

Math

FRACTIONS

A **FRACTION** is one or more equal parts of a whole. When we divide something into parts, each part is called a fraction of the whole.

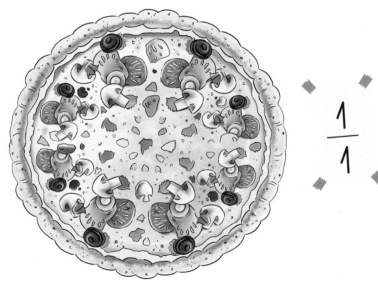

$\dfrac{1}{1}$

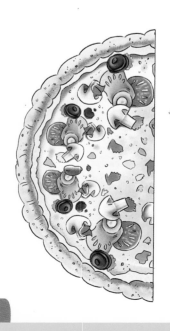

$\dfrac{1}{2}$

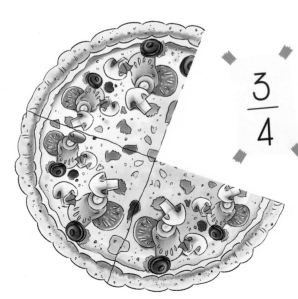

$\dfrac{3}{4}$

$\dfrac{1}{4}$

$\dfrac{1}{8}$

Fractions

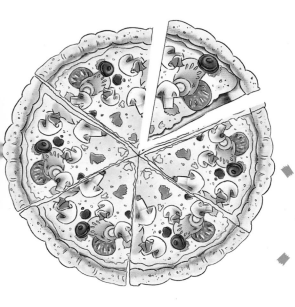

$\dfrac{1}{6}$

$\dfrac{3}{8}$

$\dfrac{4}{6}$

Math

Piece of the Pie

Color the correct fraction.

$\dfrac{7}{8}$

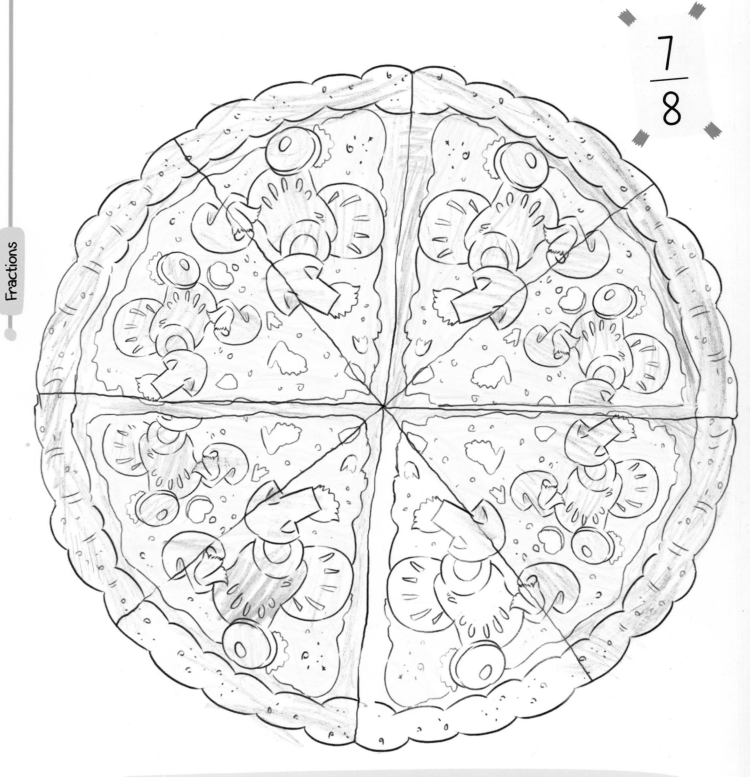

Hint: Count the total number of slices, then color 7.

Match the pictures with the correct fractions.

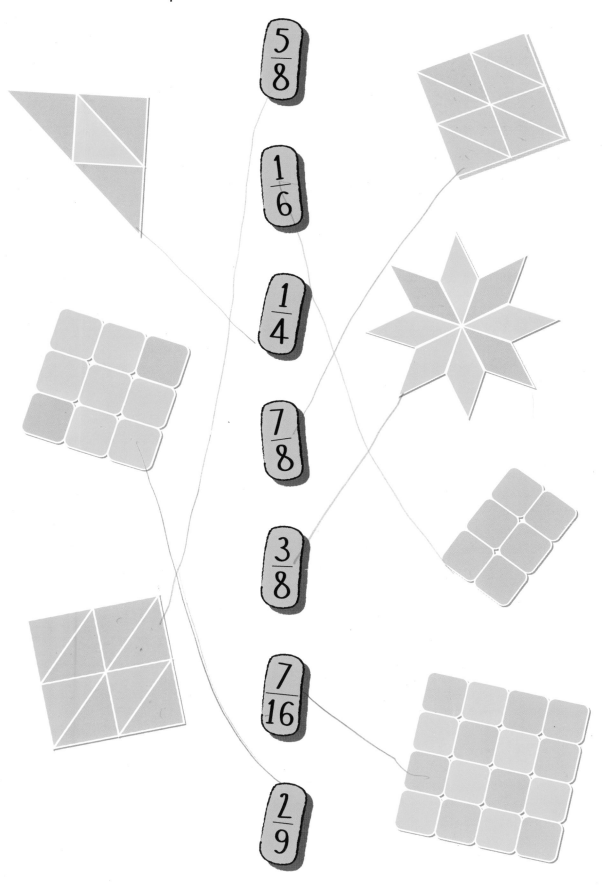

Fractions

LENGTH

LENGTH is the measure of how long, or how far away, something is.

Measuring tools

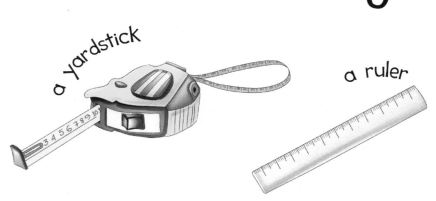

a yardstick

a ruler

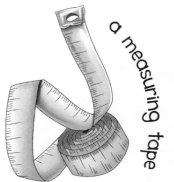

a measuring tape

Units of measurement

1 cm = 10 mm	1 foot = 30 cm
1 inch = 2.5 cm	1 yard = 3 feet
1 foot = 12 inches	1 yard = 36 inches

1 cm

1 inch

How long?

Use a ruler to measure the length of the following things:

length   4 cm

length   4 cm

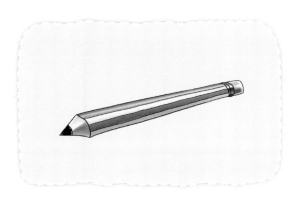

length   6 cm

length   4 cm

length   5 cm

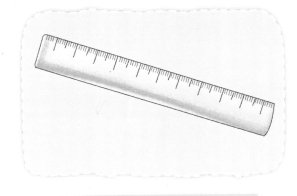

length   6 cm

TIME

TIME is the division of the day into hours, minutes and seconds.

1 day = 24 hours

1 hour = 60 minutes

1 minute = 60 seconds

A clock has three hands—the hour hand, the minute hand and the seconds hand.

hour hand

minute hand

seconds hand

What's the time?

Draw hands on the clock to show the time given.

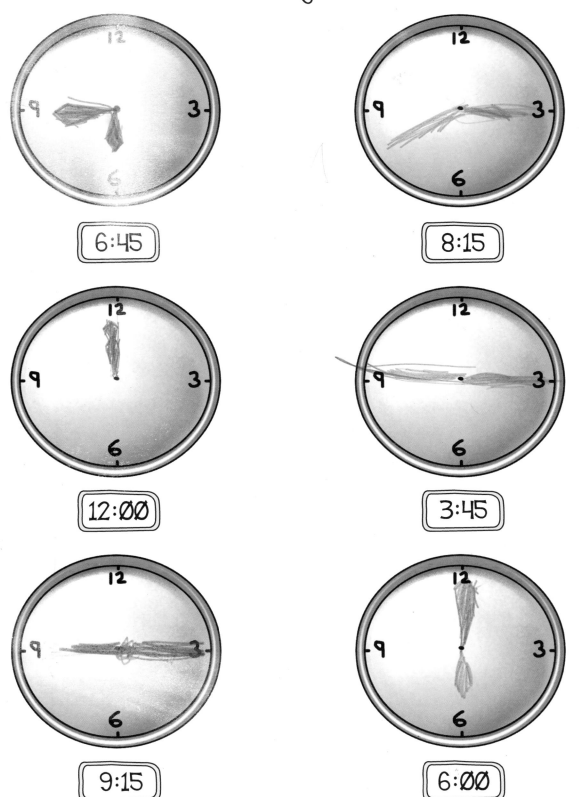

How long does it take?

Circle how long it takes you to:

Ride a bike to school

1 day	1 hour

Eat lunch

1 hour	1 minute

Smile

1 day	1 second

Hug a friend

1 minute	1 second

Yawn

1 hour	1 minute

Sneeze

1 hour	1 second

Math

Tell me when

Read the things you do during the day. Color the AM or PM box depending on when you do what.

eat breakfast

go to school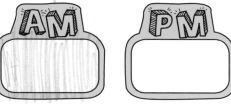

eat dinner

take a bath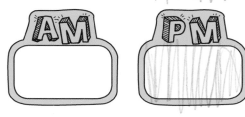

eat lunch

get dressed

go to sleep

Time

Math

MONEY

MONEY is what we use to pay for things. In most countries, money is of two kinds—notes and coins.

1 dollar	=	100 cents
half-dollar	=	50 cents
1 quarter	=	25 cents
1 dime	=	10 cents
1 nickel	=	5 cents
1 penny	=	1 cent

The color of money

Color the coins according to the code:

quarters = purple, dimes = pink,
nickels = blue, cents = yellow

Shopping list

Which coins would you need to buy?

$ 1.75

$ 1.35

$ 2.65

$ 3.55

75 ¢

$ 1.25

$ 3.15

$ 4.45

$ 2.30

dollars   quarters   dimes   nickels

dollars   quarters   dimes   nickels

dollars   quarters   dimes   nickels

Money

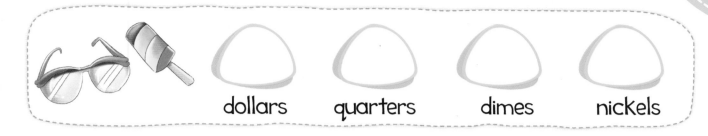

dollars quarters dimes nickels

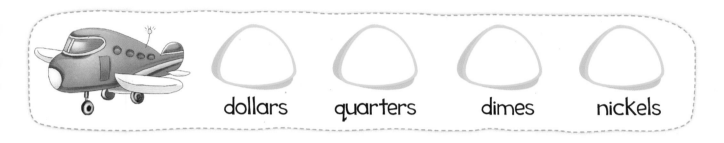

dollars quarters dimes nickels

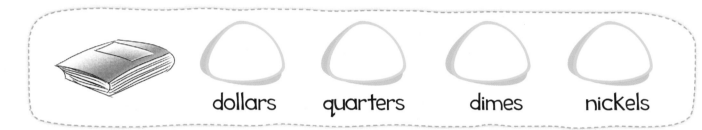

dollars quarters dimes nickels

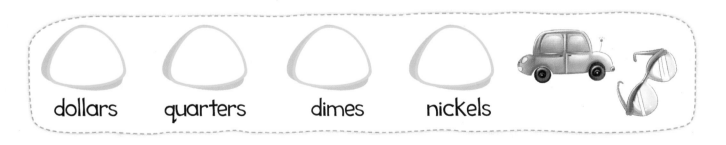

dollars quarters dimes nickels

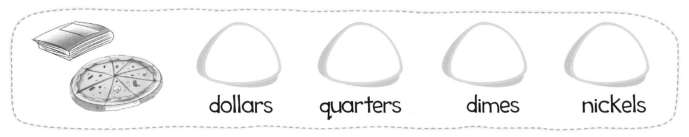

dollars quarters dimes nickels

Money

Math

Hungry piglets!

Color the correct coins to make the amount written
on the piggy bank.

$ 1.65

SHAPES

There are two kinds of shapes—2D (two-dimensional) and 3D (three-dimensional).

2D Shapes

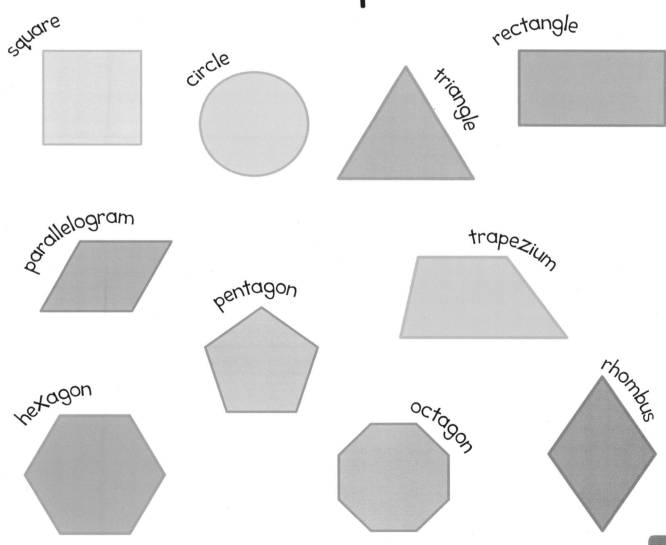

square

circle

triangle

rectangle

parallelogram

trapezium

pentagon

rhombus

hexagon

octagon

3D Shapes

cube

cuboid

cylinder

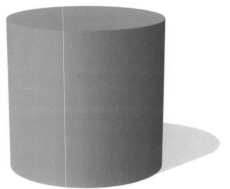

sphere

prism

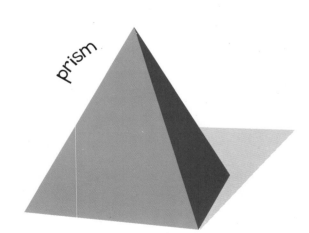

cone

Let's draw

Draw the following.

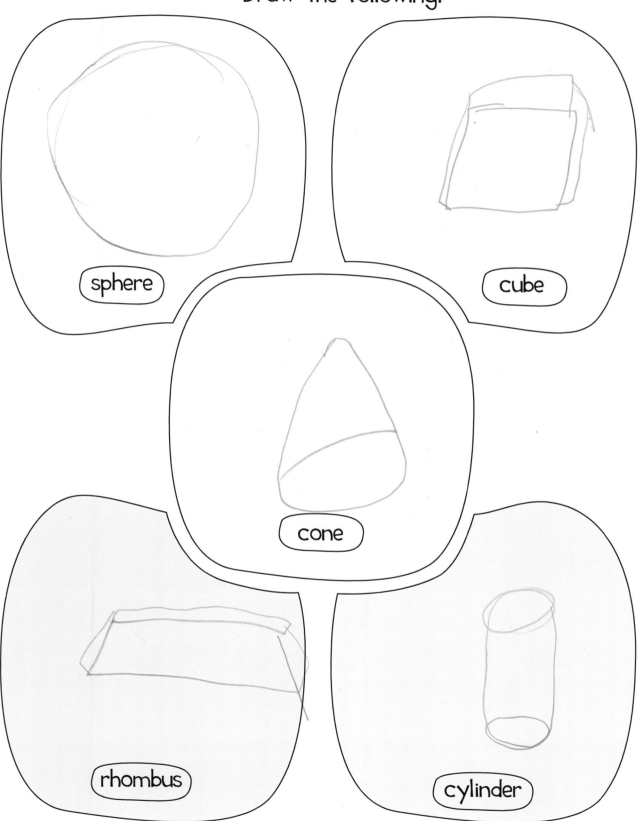

sphere

cube

cone

rhombus

cylinder

Shapes

VOLUME

VOLUME is the measurement of the amount of space inside a solid object/container.

Example:

A soda can contains 330 ml.

A milk carton has 1 liter.

Bottled water is usually 500 ml or 1 liter.

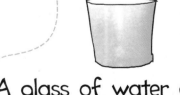

A glass of water contains 250 ml.

How much?

One milk carton contains 1 liter of milk.
Look at the pictures and color which object can
contain more or less than 1 liter.

more   less

more   less

more   less

more   less

more   less

more   less

Volume

MASS

MASS (or weight) is the measure of how heavy an object is. The units for measuring mass are kilogram (kg), gram (g) and milligram (mg).

Look at the pictures and tick (✓) which one is heavier.

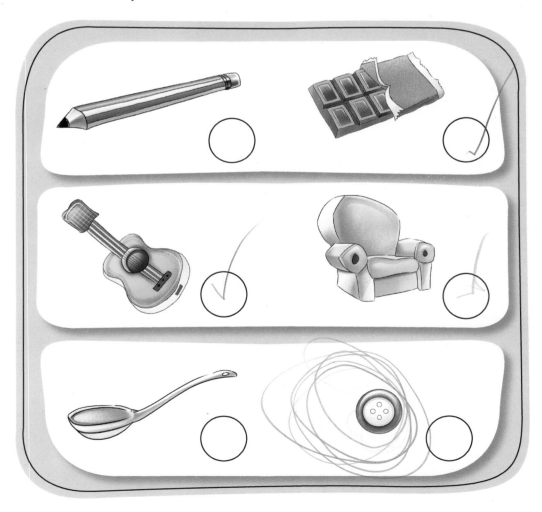

Look at the pictures and match them with how heavy they might be.

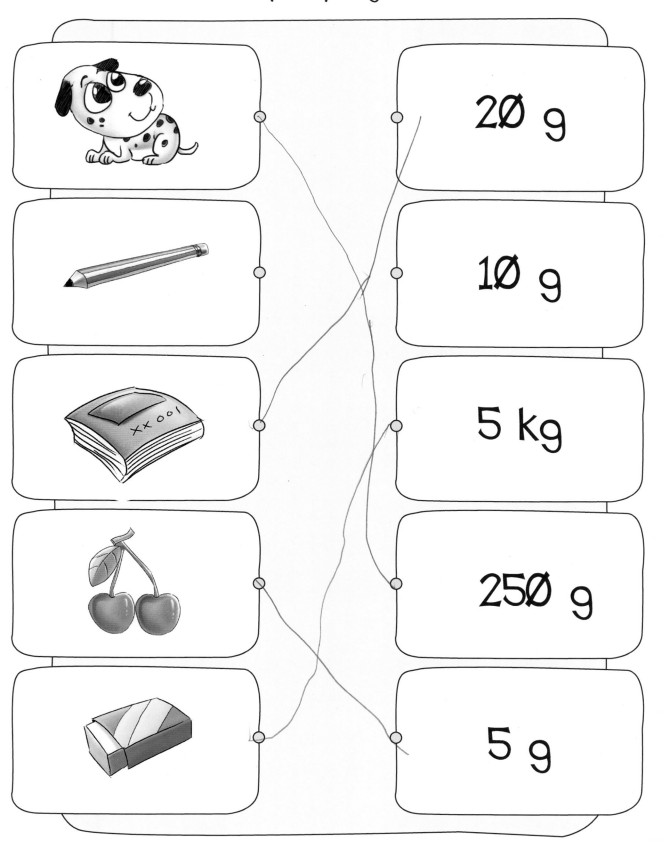

PICTOGRAPH

A **PICTOGRAPH** is a graph where pictures or symbols are used to show data.

Example:

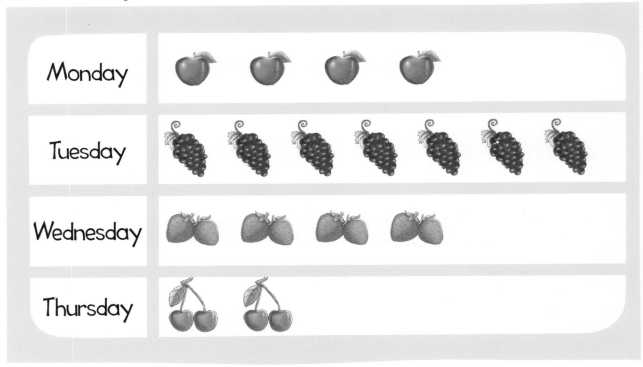

This pictograph shows how many fruits were eaten on 4 days of the week. From the pictograph, it is clear that the most fruits were eaten on Thursday, and that grapes were the favorite fruit.

How many?

Look at the pictographs and answer the questions.

In which year were the most
Christmas trees sold?

2017

= 20

In which month did the
most people swim?

May

= 20

BAR GRAPH

A BAR GRAPH uses bars to show data.

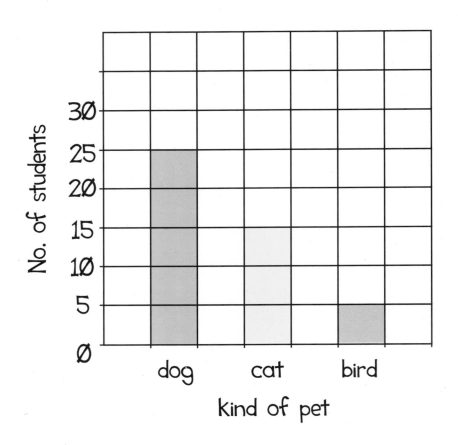

This bar graph show how many students have which kind of pet. 25 students have dogs, 15 students have cats and 5 students have birds.

No bars

Color the bar graphs according to the data given.

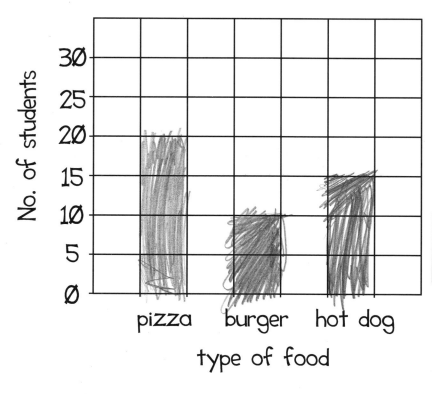

20 students like pizza
10 students like burgers
15 students like hot dogs

Bar Graph

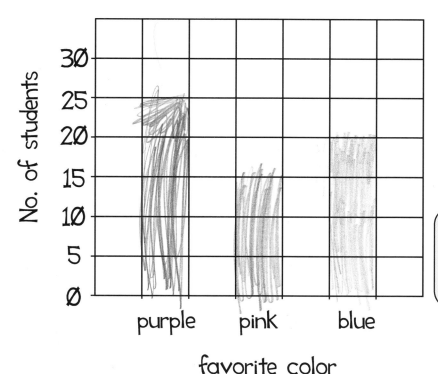

25 students like purple
15 students like pink
20 ,students like blue

Math

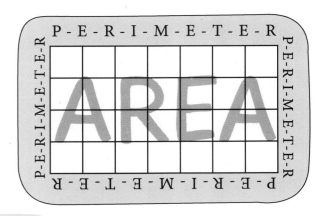

Perimeter

The measurement around the outside of an object is called its perimeter.

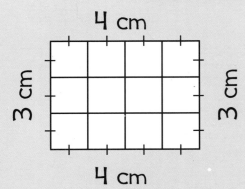

To calculate the perimeter of a figure we add all the sides.

Area

The measurement of space (square units) inside an object is called its area.

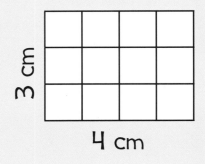

To calculate the area of a figure we count the number of squares, or multiply the sides.

AREA

AREA is the measurement of the space inside an object. Area is measured in square units—cm square, m square, km square.

Area

Example:

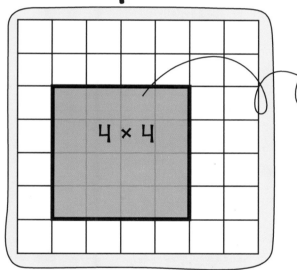

4 × 4

Area = 4 + 4 + 4 + 4
    = 16 square units

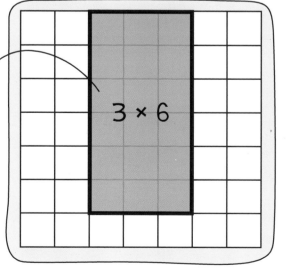

3 × 6

Area = 3 + 3 + 3 + 3 + 3 + 3
    = 18 square units

How much?

If each square is 1 square cm, find the
area of the following figures:

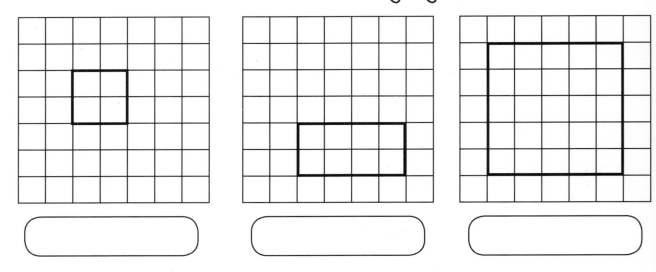

Now find the area of your eraser,
your ruler, your sharpener.

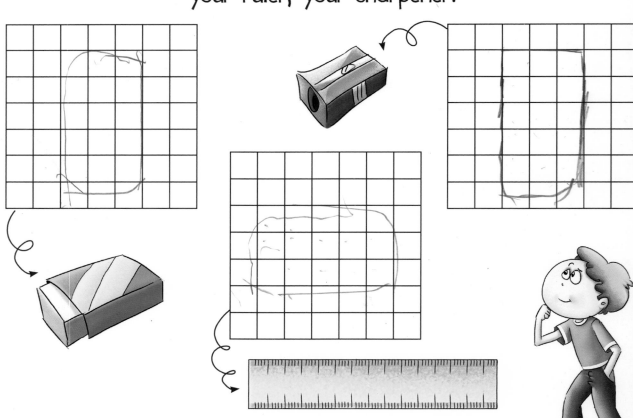

Area

PERIMETER

PERIMETER is the measurement around the outside of an object. Perimeter is measured in centimeters (cm), meters (m), kilometers (km).

Example:

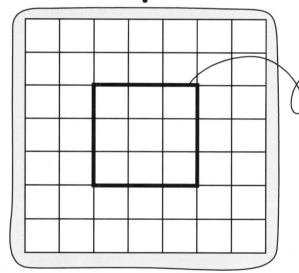

Perimeter = 3 + 3 + 3 + 3
= 12

Perimeter = 4 + 2 + 4 + 2
= 12

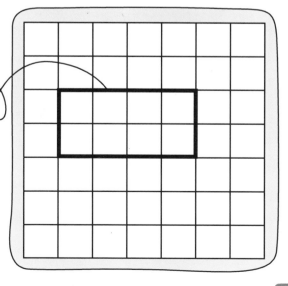

How much?

If each side of the square is 1 cm, find
the perimeter of the following figures:

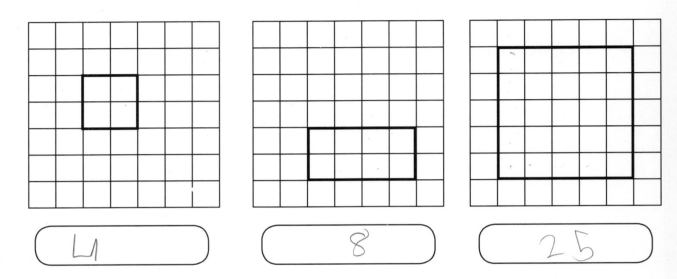

| 4 | 8 | 25 |

Now find the perimeter of your eraser,
your ruler, your sharpener.

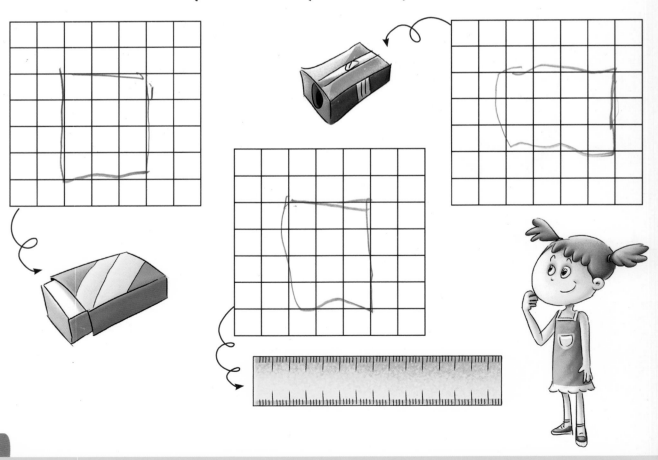

Answers

page 5

page 7

page 10

page 11

page 13

page 14

page 15

page 17

page 25

page 27

page 31

page 33

page 39

page 40

page 41

page 42

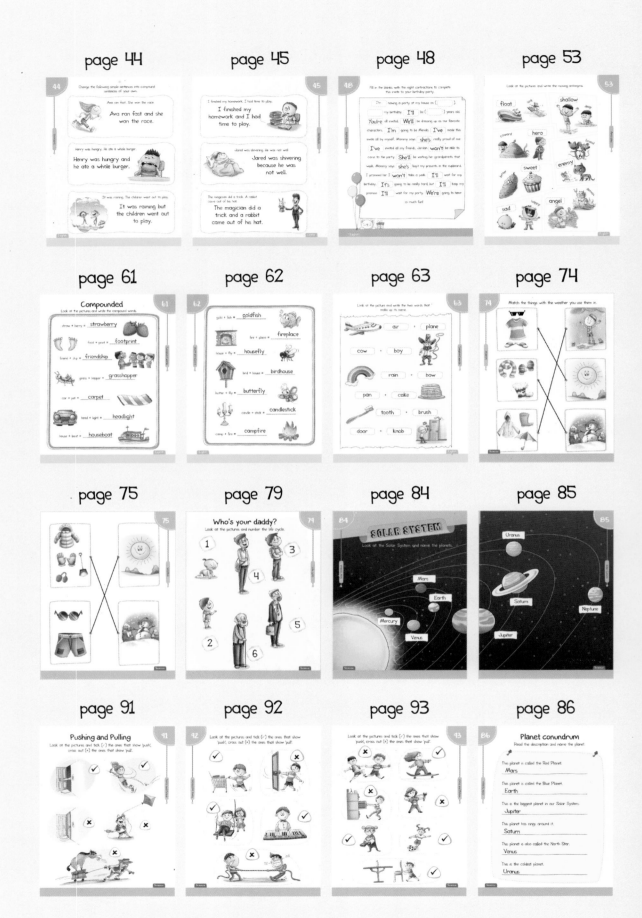

page 44

page 45

page 48

page 53

page 61

page 62

page 63

page 74

page 75

page 79

page 84

page 85

page 91

page 92

page 93

page 86

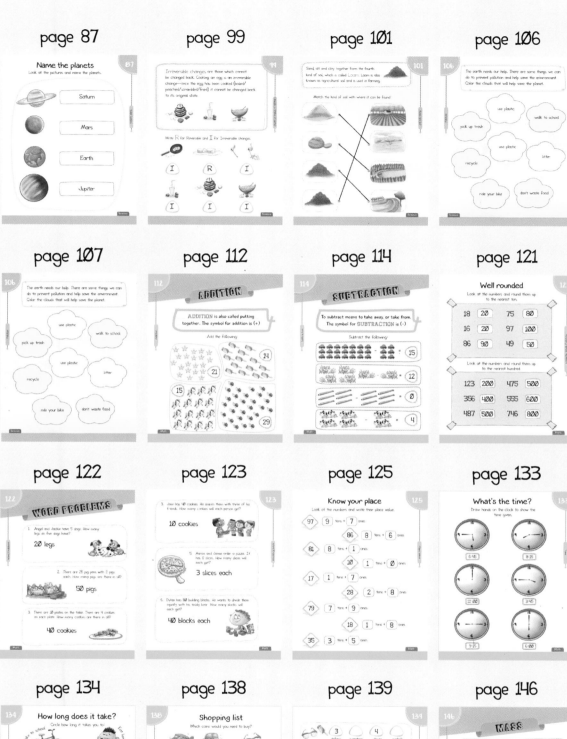

page 87

page 99

page 101

page 106

page 107

page 112

page 114

page 121

page 122

page 123

page 125

page 133

page 134

page 138

page 139

page 146

page 147

page 149

page 151

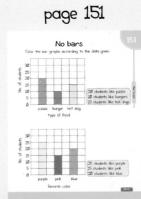

page 154

page 156

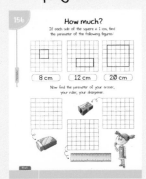